JONATHAN DOVE

Ring out, wild bells

from *The Passing of the Year*

for Double Chorus and Piano

Text by Alfred Lord Tennyson

EDITION PETERS

LEIPZIG · LONDON · NEW YORK

Commissioned by the London Symphony Chorus

First performed by the London Symphony Chorus
with Stephen Betteridge (piano) conducted by
Stephen Westrop in the Barbican Centre,
London on 18 March 2000

A new version of this work, for
double chorus, two pianos and percussion,
was commissioned for the 200th anniversary
of Edition Peters and is available on hire.

Ring out, wild bells

O Earth, O Earth, return!

Ring out, wild bells, to the wild sky,
  The flying cloud, the frosty light:
  The year is dying in the night;
Ring out, wild bells, and let him die.

Ring out the old, ring in the new,
  Ring, happy bells, across the snow:
  The year is going, let him go;
Ring out the false, ring in the true.

Ring out the grief that saps the mind,
  For those that here we see no more;
  Ring out the feud of rich and poor,
Ring in redress to all mankind.

Ring out the want, the care, the sin,
  The faithless coldness of the time;
  Ring out, ring out my mournful rhymes,
But ring the fuller minstrel in.

Ring out old shapes of foul disease;
  Ring out the narrowing lust of gold;
  Ring out the thousand wars of old,
Ring in the thousand years of peace.

Alfred Lord Tennyson

DOVE

Ring out, wild bells

from *The Passing of the Year*

for Double Chorus and Piano

EP 7568g

7. Ring out, wild bells

from *The Passing of the Year*

Jonathan Dove

Jonathan Dove

Photo © Andrew Palmer

Jonathan Dove (b. 1959) studied composition with Robin Holloway at Cambridge and worked as a freelance repetiteur, animateur and arranger. His first major projects came via Glyndebourne, including his breakthrough commission, the opera *Flight*, for Glyndebourne Touring Opera. Other operatic works include *The Adventures of Pinocchio*, *Swanhunter*, children's opera *The Hackney Chronicles*, *When She Died* – examining the response to the death of Diana, Princess of Wales – and *Man on the Moon*. Works for orchestra include the trombone concerto *Stargazer*, and *Moonlight Revels* for trumpet and saxophone. Dove was presented with the Ivor Novello Award for Classical Music in 2008, and in 2010 *A Song of Joys* opened the Last Night of the Proms.

Jonathan Dove (*1959) studierte bei Robin Holloway an der Universität Cambridge Komposition und arbeitete als freischaffender Korrepetitor und Arrangeur. Erste größere Werke entstanden in Zusammenarbeit mit dem englischen Glyndebourne Festival, darunter die Oper *Flight* – ein Auftragswerk der Glyndebourne Touring Opera, das ihm zum Durchbruch verhalf. Sein Opernschaffen umfasst außerdem *The Adventures of Pinocchio*, *Swanhunter*, die Kinderoper *The Hackney Chronicles*, *When She Died* – das die Reaktionen auf den Tod von Prinzessin Diana beleuchtet – sowie *Man on the Moon*. Zu seinen Orchesterwerken zählen das Posaunenkonzert *Stargazer* sowie *Moonlight Revels* für Trompete und Saxofon. 2008 erhielt Dove den Ivor Novello Award für klassische Musik, und 2010 bildete *A Song of Joys* den Auftakt zur „Last Night of the Proms".

EDITION PETERS GROUP

LEIPZIG · LONDON · NEW YORK

www.editionpeters.com

ISBN 9790300752846
RING OUT WILD BELLS (THE PASS
90000
9 790300 752846